85 Stroke Preventing Juice and Meal Recipes:

The Stroke-Survivors Guide to Healthy Living

By

Joe Correa CSN

COPYRIGHT

ACKNOWLEDGEMENTS

This book is dedicated to my friends and family that have had mild or serious illnesses so that you may find a solution and make the necessary changes in your life.

85 Stroke Preventing Juice and Meal Recipes:

The Stroke-Survivors Guide to

Healthy Living

By

Joe Correa CSN

CONTENTS

Copyright

Acknowledgements

About The Author

Introduction

Commitment

85 Stroke Preventing Juice and Meal Recipes: The Stroke-Survivors Guide to Healthy Living

Additional Titles from This Author

ABOUT THE AUTHOR

After years of Research, I honestly believe in the positive effects that proper nutrition can have over the body and mind. My knowledge and experience has helped me live healthier throughout the years and which I have shared with family and friends. The more you know about eating and drinking healthier, the sooner you will want to change your life and eating habits.

Nutrition is a key part in the process of being healthy and living longer so get started today. The first step is the most important and the most significant.

INTRODUCTION

85 Stroke Preventing Juice and Meal Recipes: The Stroke-Survivors Guide to Healthy Living

By Joe Correa CSN

There are several important symptoms of a stroke that shouldn't be ignored. The most common symptoms include a serious headache, confusion, trouble speaking and understanding, unexplained vomiting, inability to move parts of the body, trouble seeing in one or both eyes, trouble walking, dizziness, and lack of coordination. None of the above-described symptoms should be taken lightly and they require immediate medical attention.

The three types of strokes are:

1. Ischemic Stroke

2. Hemorrhagic Stroke

3. Transient Ischemic Attack (TIA)

Having a stroke is serious and is one of the leading causes of death in the world. Ischemic stroke is the most common type of stroke with about 85% of all strokes. The cause for this type of stroke is a partial or complete blockage of the arteries that provide blood to the brain. This medical condition results in damaged brain cells.

The cause of a hemorrhagic stroke is having leaking arteries in the brain. This extra blood puts pressure on the brain cells and damages them.

Finally, the transient ischemic attack occurs with a brief blood flow interruption. However, this type of stroke should be regarded as a medical emergency, just like any other type of stroke.

There are several important symptoms of a stroke that shouldn't be ignored. The most common symptoms include a serious headache, confusion, trouble speaking and understanding, unexplained vomiting, inability to move parts of the body, trouble seeing in one or both eyes, trouble walking, dizziness, and lack of coordination. None of the above-described symptoms should be taken lightly and require immediate medical attention.

When it comes to preventing a stroke, a healthy lifestyle and diet high in fiber and low in refined sugars is necessary.

I have created a collection of stroke preventing recipes that will boost your immune system and improve your entire health. Just a couple of minutes every day is enough to prepare these wonderful juices and the health benefits are beyond measure. Soon enough you will start feeling better than ever before. Try them all!

COMMITMENT

In order to improve my condition, I *(your name)*, commit to eating more of these foods on a daily basis and to exercise at least 30 minutes daily:

- Berries (especially blueberries), peaches, cherries, apples, apricots, oranges, lemon juice, grapefruit, tangerines, mandarins, pears, etc.
- Broccoli, spinach, collard greens, sweet potatoes, avocado, artichoke, baby corn, carrots, celery, cauliflower, onions, etc.
- Whole grains, steel-cut oats, oatmeal, quinoa, barley, etc.
- Black beans, red bean beans, garbanzo beans, lentils, etc.
- Nuts and seeds including: walnuts, cashews, flaxseeds, sesame seeds, etc.
- Fish
- 8 – 10 glasses of water

Sign here

X_____

85 STROKE PREVENTING JUICE AND MEAL RECIPES: THE STROKE-SURVIVORS GUIDE TO HEALTHY LIVING

JUICES

1.   Celery Sweet Potato Juice

Ingredients:

1 cup of celery, chopped

1 cup of sweet potato, chopped

1 cup of Swiss chard, torn

1 large cucumber

A handful of spinach, torn

2 oz of water

Preparation:

Wash the celery and chop into small pieces. Set aside.

Peel the sweet potato and cut into chunks. Fill the measuring cup and reserve the rest for some other juice.

Combine Swiss chard and spinach in a colander. Wash thoroughly under cold running water and torn with hands. Drain and set aside.

Wash the cucumber and cut into thick slices. Set aside.

Now, combine celery, sweet potato, Swiss chard, cucumber, and spinach in a juicer and process until juiced. Transfer to serving glasses and stir in the water.

Refrigerate for 10 minutes before serving.

Enjoy!

Nutritional information per serving: Kcal: 156, Protein: 6.3g, Carbs: 43.2g, Fats: 0.8g

2. Cherry Cantaloupe Juice

Ingredients:

1 cup of cherries

1 large green apple, cored

1 cup of cantaloupe, chopped

1 large carrot

2 oz of water

Preparation:

Place the cherries in a colander and wash under cold running water. Drain and cut in half. Remove the pits and set aside.

Wash the apple and remove the core. Cut into bite-sized pieces and set aside.

Cut the cantaloupe in half. Scoop out the seeds and cut two large wedges.Peel and chop into chunks. Reserve the rest of the cantaloupe in a refrigerator for some other juice.

Wash the carrot and cut into thick slices. Set aside.

Now, combine cherries, apple, cantaloupe, and carrot in a juicer and process until juiced.

Transfer to serving glasses and stir in the water. Add some ice or refrigerate before serving.

Nutritional information per serving: Kcal: 249, Protein: 4.5g, Carbs: 72.3g, Fats: 1.1g

3.　　Strawberry Cranberry Juice

Ingredients:

1 cup of strawberries

1 large Fuji apple, cored

1 cup of cranberries

1 large carrot

1 large lemon

1 large orange

Preparation:

Place the strawberries and cranberries in a colander and wash under cold running water. Drain and cut in half. Set aside.

Wash the apple and remove the core. Cut into bite-sized pieces and set aside.

Wash the carrot and cut into thick slices. Set aside.

Peel the lemon cut lengthwise in half. Set aside.

Peel the orange and divide into wedges. Set aside.

Now, process strawberries, apple, cranberries, carrots, lemon, and orange in juicer. Transfer to serving glasses and stir in the water.

Add few ice cubes, or refrigerate for 15 minutes before serving.

Nutritional information per serving: Kcal: 268, Protein: 5.6g, Carbs: 89.1g, Fats: 1.6g

4.   Broccoli Pumpkin Juice

Ingredients:

1 cup of broccoli, chopped

1 cup of pumpkin, cubed

1 whole lemon, peeled

1 cup of fennel, chopped

1 cup of cucumber, sliced

Preparation:

Wash the broccoli and trim off the outer leaves. Cut into bite-sized pieces and fill the measuring cup. Reserve the rest for later.

Cut the top of a pumpkin. Cut lengthwise in half and then scrape out the seeds. Cut one large wedge and peel it. Cut into small cubes and fill the measuring cup. Reserve the rest in the refrigerator.

Peel the lemon and cut lengthwise in half. Set aside.

Trim off the outer wilted layers of the fennel. Roughly chop it and fill the measuring cup. Reserve the rest for later.

Wash the cucumber and cut into thin slices. Fill the measuring cup and reserve the rest in the refrigerator. Set aside.

Now, combine broccoli, pumpkin, lemon, fennel, and cucumber in a juicer and process until well juiced. Transfer to a serving glass and add some crushed ice.

Serve immediately.

Nutrition information per serving: Kcal: 196, Protein: 2.8g, Carbs: 55.5g, Fats: 1.3g

5.   Berry Beet Juice

Ingredients:

1 cup of blackberries

1 cup of blueberries

1 cup of fresh basil

1 large beet, trimmed

2 oz of coconut water

Preparation:

Combine blackberries and blueberries in a colander and wash under cold running water. Set aside.

Wash the beet and trim off the green ends. Chop into small pieces and set aside.

Wash the basil thoroughly and roughly chop it using hands.

Now, combine blackberries, blueberries, beet and basil in a juicer and process until juiced.

Transfer to serving glasses and stir in the coconut water.

Add some ice and serve immediately.

Nutritional information per serving: Kcal: 142, Protein: 5.2g, Carbs: 44.8g, Fats: 1.5g

6. Avocado Radish Juice

Ingredients:

1 cup of avocado, cubed

3 large radishes, chopped

1 small zucchini, sliced

1 cup of celery, chopped

1 cup of cucumber, sliced

¼ tsp of salt

1 oz of water

Preparation:

Peel the avocado and cut in half. Remove the pit and cut into small cubes. Fill the measuring cup and reserve the rest for later.

Wash the radishes and cut into small pieces. Set aside.

Wash the zucchini and cut into thin slices. Set aside.

Wash the celery and chop it into bite-sized pieces. Set aside.

Wash the cucumber and cut into thin slices. Fill the measuring cup and reserve the rest for later. Set aside.

Now, combine avocado, radishes, zucchini, celery, and cucumber in a juicer and process until juiced. Transfer to a serving glass and stir in the salt and water.

Serve cold.

Nutrition information per serving: Kcal: 235, Protein: 5.6g, Carbs: 22.3g, Fats: 22.6g

7.   Green Cayenne Juice

Ingredients:

1 cup of fresh broccoli

1 large carrot

1 large leek

1 cup of kale, chopped

1 large lime, peeled

1 large lemon, peeled

1 large cucumber

¼ tsp of Cayenne pepper, ground

Preparation:

Wash the broccoli and cut into small pieces and set aside.

Wash the carrot and cucumber and cut into thick slices. Set aside.

Wash the kale and celery thoroughly under cold running water. Roughly chop it and set aside.

Peel the lemon and lime and cut lengthwise in half. Set aside.

Now, process broccoli, carrot, kale, leek, lemon, and lime in a juicer.

Transfer to serving glasses and stir in the Cayenne pepper for extra spicy flavor.

Refrigerate for 30 minutes before serving.

Nutrition information per serving: Kcal: 174, Protein: 10.2g, Carbs: 51.4g, Fats: 1.9g

8.   Guava Squash Juice

Ingredients:

1 cup of butternut squash, chopped

1 large guava

1 large carrot

1 large cucumber

1 large orange

1 tbsp of honey

Preparation:

Peel the butternut squash and remove the seeds using a spoon. Cut into small cubes and reserve the rest of the squash for some other recipe. Wrap in a plastic foil and refrigerate.

Peel the guava and cut into chunks. Set aside.

Wash the carrot and cucumber and cut into thick slices. Set aside.

Now, combine butternut squash, guava, carrot, and cucumber in a juicer and process until juiced.

Transfer to serving glasses and stir in the honey.

Add some ice and serve immediately.

Nutritional information per serving: Kcal: 266, Protein: 7.2g, Carbs: 80.7g, Fats: 1.4g

9.   Blueberry Cucumber Juice

Ingredients:

1 cup of blueberries

1 cup of cucumber, sliced

1 cup of strawberries, chopped

1 cup of fresh mint, torn

1 large carrot, sliced

¼ tsp of cinnamon, ground

Preparation:

Wash the blueberries using a small colander. Drain and set aside.

Wash the cucumber and cut into thin slices. Fill the measuring cup and reserve the rest in the refrigerator.

Wash the strawberries and remove the stems. Chop into small pieces and set aside.

Wash the mint thoroughly under cold running water. Drain and torn into small pieces. Set aside.

Wash and peel the carrot. Cut into thin slices and set aside.

Now, combine blueberries, cucumber, strawberries, mint, and carrot in a juicer. Process until well juiced.

Transfer to a serving glass and stir in the cinnamon. Add some crushed ice and serve immediately!

Nutrition information per serving: Kcal: 141, Protein: 4g, Carbs: 45g, Fats: 1.3g

10.   Thick Banana Juice

Ingredients:

2 large bananas

1 cup of grapes

1 tsp of pure vanilla extract, sugar-free

½ cup of coconut milk, sugar-free

Preparation:

Peel the bananas and chop into small chunks. Set aside.

Wash the grapes under cold running water. Drain and set aside.

Combine bananas and grapes in a juicer and process until juiced. Transfer to serving glasses and stir in the coconut milk and vanilla extract.

Add some ice and serve!

Nutritional information per serving: Kcal: 293, Protein: 7.5g, Carbs: 77.9g, Fats: 4g

11.   Summer Guava Juice

Ingredients:

1 cup of pineapple chunks

1 whole guava, chopped

2 cups of chard, chopped

2 whole lemons, peeled

½ cup of coconut water, unsweetened

Preparation:

Cut the top of a pineapple and peel it using a sharp knife. Cut into small chunks. Reserve the rest of the pineapple in a refrigerator.

Wash the guava and cut into chunks. If you are using large fruit, reserve the rest for some other recipe in a refrigerator.

Wash the chard thoroughly under cold running water and set aside.

Peel the lemons and cut lengthwise in half. Set aside.

Now, process pineapple, guava, chard, and lemons in a juicer. Transfer to serving glasses and stir in the coconut water.

Add some ice and serve immediately.

Nutritional information per serving: Kcal: 130, Protein: 4.8g, Carbs: 43g, Fats: 1.2g

12.   Cauliflower Tomato Juice

Ingredients:

1 cup of cauliflower, chopped

1 medium-sized tomato, chopped

½ cup of spring onions, chopped

½ cup of basil, torn

1 cup of cucumber, sliced

1 oz of water

Preparation:

Trim off the outer leaves of the cauliflower. Wash it and cut into small pieces. Fill the measuring cup and reserve the rest for later. Set aside.

Wash the tomato and place in a small bowl. Chop into small pieces and reserve the tomato juice while cutting. Set aside.

Wash the spring onions and basil. Chop into small pieces. Set aside.

Wash the cucumber and cut into thin slices. Fill the measuring cup and reserve the rest for later. Set aside.

Now, combine cauliflower, tomato, spring onions, basil, and cucumber in a juicer and process until well juiced. Transfer to a serving glass and stir in the water.

Serve cold.

Nutrition information per serving: Kcal: 51, Protein: 4.4g, Carbs: 13.9g, Fats: 0.7g

13.   Fresh Apple and Cucumber Juice

Ingredients:

3 large Granny Smith apples, cored

1 large lemon, peeled

4 cups of cucumber

¼ cup of water

1 tbsp of liquid honey

Preparation:

Wash the apples and remove the core. Cut into bite-sized pieces and set aside.

Peel the lemon and cut lengthwise in half. Set aside.

Wash the cucumber and cut into thick slices. Set aside.

Now, combine apples, lemon and cucumber in a juicer and process until juiced. Transfer to serving glasses and stir in the water and liquid honey.

Garnish with some fresh mint, but this is optional.

Add few ice cubes before serving and enjoy!

Nutrition information per serving: Kcal: 327, Protein: 4.7g, Carbs: 97g, Fats: 1.5g

14. Carrot Celery Juice

Ingredients:

1 large carrot, sliced

1 cup of celery, chopped

1 whole lemon, peeled

1 small Golden Delicious apple, cored

¼ tsp turmeric, ground

¼ tsp ginger, ground

Preparation:

Wash and peel the carrot. Cut into small slices and set aside.

Wash the celery and cut into small pieces. Set aside.

Peel the lemon and cut lengthwise in half. Set aside.

Wash the apple and cut in half. Remove the core and cut into bite-sized pieces. Set aside.

Now, combine carrot, celery, lemon, and apple in a juicer and process until juiced. Transfer to a serving glass and stir in the water, turmeric, and ginger. If you like, add some crushed ice.

Serve immediately.

Nutrition information per serving: Kcal: 105, Protein: 2.4g, Carbs: 32.8g, Fats: 0.7g

15.   Green Kiwi Juice

Ingredients:

3 large kiwis, peeled

1 cup of kale, torn

1 cup of cranberries

1 tsp of pure coconut sugar

Preparation:

Peel the kiwis and cut lengthwise in half. Set aside.

Wash the kale thoroughly and torn with hands. Set aside.

Wash the cranberries under cold running water. Drain and set aside.

Now, combine kiwis, kale, and cranberries in a juicer. Transfer to serving glasses and stir in the coconut water.

Add some ice and serve!

Nutritional information per serving: Kcal: 153, Protein: 5.6g, Carbs: 48.4g, Fats: 1.8g

16.   Avocado Juice

Ingredients:

1 whole avocado, chopped

7 oz of artichokes, chopped

1 medium-sized lemon, peeled

1 cup of red cabbage, torn

1 cup of green cabbage, torn

Preparation:

Peel the avocado and cut in half. Remove the pit and cut into chunks. Set aside.

Trim off the outer leaves of the artichoke using a sharp knife. Cut into small pieces and set aside.

Peel the lemon and cut lengthwise in half. Set aside.

Combine red and green cabbage in a colander and wash under cold running water. Drain and torn with hands. Set aside.

Now, combine avocado, artichoke, lemon, and cabbages in a juicer and process until juiced.

Transfer to serving glasses and add some ice before serving.

Enjoy!

Nutritional information per serving: Kcal: 353, Protein: 12.3g, Carbs: 51g, Fats: 30g

17.   Beet Raspberry Juice

Ingredients:

1 cup of beets, sliced

1 cup of raspberries

1 whole lemon, peeled

1 medium-sized pear, chopped

1 oz of water

Preparation:

Wash the beets and trim off the green parts. Cut into thin slices and fill the measuring cup. Reserve the rest for later.

Rinse well the raspberries using a small colander. Drain and set aside.

Peel the lemon and cut lengthwise in half. Set aside.

Wash the pear and cut in half. Remove the core and cut into bite-sized pieces. Set aside.

Now, combine beets, raspberries, lemon, and pear in a juicer and process until juiced. Transfer to a serving glass and stir in the water.

Refrigerate for 10 minutes before serving.

Nutrition information per serving: Kcal: 165, Protein: 4.9g, Carbs: 60.2g, Fats: 1.4g

18.   Raspberry Avocado Juice

Ingredients:

2 cups of fresh raspberries

1 cup of avocado, sliced

1 cup of kale, chopped

½ cup of pure coconut water, unsweetened

1 tsp of coconut sugar

Preparation:

Wash the raspberries under cold running water and set aside.

Peel the avocado and cut in half. Remove the pit and cut into chunks. Fill the measuring cup and reserve the rest for some other juice. Set aside.

Wash the kale thoroughly and torn with hands. Set aside.

Now, combine raspberries, avocado, and kale in a juicer and process until juiced.

Transfer to serving glasses and add some ice before serving.

Nutrition information per serving: Kcal: 351, Protein: 17.3g, Carbs: 65.2g, Fats: 25.4g

19.   Kiwi Apricot Juice

Ingredients:

2 whole kiwis, peeled and halved

3 whole apricots, chopped

1 large green apple, cored

1 large banana, chunked

Preparation:

Peel the kiwi and cut lengthwise in half. Set aside.

Wash the apricots and cut in half. Remove the pits and cut into small pieces. Set aside.

Wash the apple and cut lengthwise in half. Remove the core and cut into bite-sized pieces. Set aside.

Peel the banana and cut into small chunks. Set aside.

Now, combine kiwi, apricots, apple, and banana in a juicer and process until juiced. Transfer to a serving glass and add some ice.

Serve immediately.

Nutrition information per serving: Kcal: 313, Protein: 5.4g, Carbs: 91g, Fats: 1.9g

20.   Pear Apricot Juice

Ingredients:

1 large pear, chopped

3 whole apricots, pitted

1 cup of pomegranate seeds

1 medium-sized orange, wedged

¼ tsp of cinnamon, ground

Preparation:

Wash the pear and cut lengthwise in half. Cut into bite-sized pieces and set aside.

Wash the apricots and cut each in half. Remove the pit and cut into small pieces. Set aside.

Cut the top of the pomegranate fruit using a sharp paring knife. Slice down to each of the white membranes inside of the fruit. Pop the seeds into a measuring cup and set aside.

Peel the orange and divide into wedges. Cut each wedge in half and set aside.

Now, combine pear, apricots, pomegranate seeds, and orange in a juicer. Process until well juiced. Transfer to a serving glass and stir in the cinnamon.

Refrigerate for 10 minutes before serving.

Nutrition information per serving: Kcal: 253, Protein: 4.9g, Carbs: 78.3g, Fats: 1.9g

21.   Leek Radish Juice

Ingredients:

2 large leeks, chopped

3 large radishes, chopped

2 cups of beet greens, torn

1 cup of collard greens, torn

1 large cucumber

½ tsp of Himalayan salt

¼ tsp of Cayenne pepper, ground

3 oz of water

Preparation:

Wash the leeks and chop into small pieces. Set aside.

Wash the radishes and trim off the green parts. Cut in half and set aside.

Combine beet greens and collard greens in a colander. Wash thoroughly under cold running water. Drain and set aside.

Wash the cucumber and cut into thick slices. Set aside-

Now, combine leeks, radishes, beet greens, collard greens, and cucumber in a juicer and process until juiced.

Transfer to serving glasses and stir in the salt, Cayenne pepper, and water.

Refrigerate for 15 minutes before serving.

Enjoy!

Nutritional information per serving: Kcal: 148, Protein: 7.6g, Carbs: 42.3g, Fats: 1.2g

22.   Peachy Asparagus Juice

Ingredients:

1 large peach

1 cup of fresh asparagus, chopped

1 cup of collard greens

1 large grapefruit, peeled

1 cup of Romaine lettuce, shredded

1 cup of fennel, sliced

Preparation:

Wash the peach and cut in half. Remove the pit and cut into bite-sized pieces. Set aside.

Combine collard greens and lettuce in a colander and wash under cold running water. Torn with hands and set aside.

Peel the grapefruit and cut into small pieces. Set aside.

Wash the fennel bulb and trim off the wilted outer layers. Cut into small chunks and set aside.

Wash the asparagus and trim off the woody ends. Chop into small pieces and set aside.

Now, combine peach, collard greens, lettuce, grapefruit, and fennel in a juicer and process until juiced.

Transfer to serving glasses and add some ice before serving.

Nutritional information per serving: Kcal: 187, Protein: 9.1g, Carbs: 57.9g, Fats: 1.4g

23.   Winter Squash Juice

Ingredients:

2 cups of butternut squash, seeded

2 large carrots

1 large Granny Smith Apple

1 small ginger root slice

Preparation:

Peel the butternut squash and remove the seeds using a spoon. Cut into small cubes and fill the measuring cup. Reserve the rest of the squash for some other juice. Wrap in a plastic foil and refrigerate.

Wash the carrots and cut into thick slices. Set aside.

Wash the apple and remove the core. Cut into bite-sized pieces and set aside.

Peel the ginger slice and set aside.

Now, process butternut squash, carrots, apple, and ginger in a juicer.

Transfer to serving glasses and refrigerate before serving.

Nutrition information per serving: Kcal: 246, Protein: 5.1g, Carbs: 75g, Fats: 1.1g

24.   Grapefruit Raspberry Juice

Ingredients:

1 large grapefruit

1 cup of raspberries

1 large lemon

1 large lime

1 medium-sized yellow apple, cored

4oz of coconut water

Preparation:

Peel the grapefruit and divide into wedges. Set aside.

Place the raspberries in a colander and wash under cold running water. Drain and set aside.

Peel the lemon and lime. Cut lengthwise in half and set aside.

Wash the apple and remove the core. Cut into bite-sized pieces and set aside.

Now combine grapefruit, raspberries, lemon, lime, and apple in a juicer and process until juiced. Transfer to serving glasses and stir in the coconut water.

Add some ice and serve immediately.

Note:

Lemon and lime contain a high amount of citrate, so make sure to add more water than usual.

Nutritional information per serving: Kcal: 240, Protein: 4.6g, Carbs: 76g, Fats: 1.6g

25.   Fresh Grape Juice

Ingredients:

2 cups of grapes

1 cup of kale, chopped

1 whole grapefruit, peeled

1 cup of watercress, chopped

½ cup of water

Preparation:

Place the grapes in a colander and wash under cold running water. Set aside.

Combine kale and watercress in a colander and wash thoroughly. Chop it roughly using hands and set aside.

Wash the grapefruit and cut into chunks. Set aside.

Now, process grapes, kale, watercress, and grapefruit in a juicer. Transfer to serving glasses and stir in the water.

Refrigerate for 20 minutes before serving.

Nutritional information per serving: Kcal: 231, Protein: 6.7g, Carbs: 64g, Fats: 1.6g

26. Pomegranate Apple Juice

Ingredients:

1 cup of pomegranate seeds

1 medium-sized Granny Smith's apple, cored

1 large banana, chunked

1 tbsp of liquid honey

1 oz of water

Preparation:

Cut the top of the pomegranate fruit using a sharp paring knife. Slice down to each of the white membranes inside of the fruit. Pop the seeds into a measuring cup and set aside.

Wash the apple and cut lengthwise in half. Remove the core and cut into bite-sized pieces. Set aside.

Peel the banana and cut into small chunks. Set aside.

Now, combine pomegranate, apple, and banana in a juicer and process until juiced. Transfer to a serving glass and stir in the honey and water.

Serve cold.

Nutrition information per serving: Kcal: 243, Protein: 3.6g, Carbs: 70.1g, Fats: 1.8g

27.   Pepper Broccoli Juice

Ingredients:

1 large green bell pepper, chopped

1 cup of broccoli, chopped

1 cup of Brussels sprouts, halved

1 whole lime, peeled

2 large carrots, sliced

¼ tsp turmeric, ground

Preparation:

Wash the bell pepper and cut lengthwise in half. Remove the stem and seeds. Chop into small pieces and set aside.

Wash the broccoli and Brussels sprouts. Trim off the wilted and outer leaves. Place in a heavy-bottomed pot and add water enough to cover all. Bring it to a boil and then remove from the heat. Drain well and chop into small pieces. Set aside to cool completely.

Peel the lime and cut lengthwise in half. Set aside.

Wash and peel the carrots. Cut into thin slices and set aside.

Now, combine bell pepper, broccoli, Brussels sprouts, lime, and carrots in a juicer and process until juiced. Transfer to a serving glasses and stir in the turmeric. Add some water, if needed.

Sprinkle with some salt, but it's optional.

Nutrition information per serving: Kcal: 122, Protein: 8.5g, Carbs: 39.1g, Fats: 1.2g

28.   Parsnip Zucchini Juice

Ingredients:

1 cup of parsnips, chopped

1 large zucchini, seeded

1 cup of sweet potatoes, chopped

1 ginger root slice, 1-inch

2 oz of water

Preparation:

Wash the parsnips and trim off the green parts. Cut into thick slices and fill the measuring cup. Reserve the rest for some other juice.

Peel the zucchini and cut in half. Scrape out the seeds with a spoon. Cut into chunks and set aside.

Peel the sweet potato and cut into chunks. Fill the measuring cup and reserve the rest for some other juice. Set aside.

Peel the ginger root and set aside.

Now, process parsnips, zucchini, sweet potato, and ginger in a juicer.

Transfer to serving glasses and stir in the water.

Refrigerate for 10 minutes before serving.

Nutrition information per serving: Kcal: 216, Protein: 7.6g, Carbs: 61.1g, Fats: 1.5g

29. Plum Peach Juice

Ingredients:

5 large plums, pitted

2 large peaches, pitted

1 cup of pomegranate seeds

1 large carrot

Preparation:

Wash the plums and peaches and cut in half. Remove the pits and set aside.

Cut the top of the pomegranate fruit using a sharp knife. Slice down to each of the white membranes inside of the fruit. Pop the seeds into a small bowl. Set aside.

Wash the carrot and cut into small pieces. Set aside.

Now, combine plums, peaches, pomegranate seeds, and carrot in a juicer and process until juiced.

Transfer to serving glasses and refrigerate for 30 minutes before serving.

Nutritional information per serving: Kcal: 326, Protein: 7.6g, Carbs: 94.2g, Fats: 3.1g

30. Sweet Mango Juice

Ingredients:

1 cup of mango, chopped

1 cup of apricots, sliced

½ cup of pure coconut water, unsweetened

1 tbsp of coconut sugar

Preparation:

Peel the mango and cut into small chunks. Set aside.

Wash the apricots and cut in half. Remove the pits and chop into small pieces. Set aside.

Now, combine mango and apricots in a juicer and process until juiced.

Transfer to serving glasses and stir in the coconut water and coconut sugar.

Add few ice cubes and serve immediately.

Nutritional information per serving: Kcal: 155, Protein: 3.6g, Carbs: 43g, Fats: 1.2g

31.   Mustard Greens Apple Juice

Ingredients:

1 cup of mustard greens, chopped

1 Granny Smith apple, peeled and cored

1 large artichoke, chopped

1 cup of Brussels sprouts

½ tsp of cinnamon, freshly ground

½ cup of pure coconut water, unsweetened

1 tsp of agave nectar

Preparation:

Wash the mustard greens and chop with hands. Set aside.

Wash the apple and remove the core. Cut into bite-sized pieces and set aside.

Using a sharp knife, trim off the outer leave of the artichoke. Cut into small pieces and set aside.

Wash the Brussels sprouts and trim off the outer layers. Set aside.

Now, process mustard greens, apple, artichoke, and Brussels sprouts in a juicer.

Transfer to serving glasses and stir in the cinnamon, coconut water, and agave nectar.

Add some ice and serve immediately.

Nutritional information per serving: Kcal: 195, Protein: 13.7g, Carbs: 63.4g, Fats: 1.3g

32.   Parsnip Juice

Ingredients:

1 cup of parsnips, sliced

1 large banana, peeled

1 large orange, peeled

1 cup of cauliflower, chopped

A handful of fresh mint, chopped

1 tsp of honey, raw

Preparation:

Wash the parsnips and cut into thick slices. Set aside.

Peel the banana and cut into chunks. Set aside.

Peel the orange and divide into wedges. Set aside.

Trim off the outer leaves of cauliflower. Wash it and cut into small pieces. Reserve the rest in the refrigerator.

Now, process parsnips, banana, orange, and cauliflower in a juicer.

Transfer to serving glasses and stir in the honey. Sprinkle with mint and refrigerate for 20 minutes before serving.

Enjoy!

Nutritional information per serving: Kcal: 336, Protein: 8.5g, Carbs: 103g, Fats: 1.5g

33.   Strawberry Spinach Juice

Ingredients:

1 cup of strawberries, chopped

1 cup of spinach, torn

1 whole lemon, peeled

1 whole lime, peeled

1 tbsp honey, raw

2 oz of water

Preparation:

Wash the strawberries and remove the stems. Cut into bite-sized pieces and set aside.

Wash the spinach thoroughly under cold running water. Slightly drain and torn into small pieces. Set aside.

Peel the lemon and lime. Cut each fruit lengthwise in half and set aside.

Now, combine strawberries, spinach, lemon, and lime in a juicer and process until juiced. Transfer to a serving glass and stir in the water and honey.

Garnish with some mint, but it's optional.

Refrigerate for 15 minutes before serving.

Enjoy!

Nutrition information per serving: Kcal: 81, Protein: 5.8g, Carbs: 27.8g, Fats: 1.4g

34.   Pumpkin Rosemary Juice

Ingredients:

1 cup of pumpkin, cubed

1 large yellow bell pepper, seeded

1 large orange, peeled

1 large lime, peeled

1 small rosemary sprig

Preparation:

Peel the pumpkin and cut in half. Scoop out the seeds using a spoon. Cut one large wedge and peel it. Cut into small chunks and fill the measuring cup. Reserve the rest for some other juice.

Wash the bell pepper and cut in half. Remove the seeds and cut into small slices. Set aside.

Peel the orange and divide into wedges. Set aside.

Peel the lime and cut lengthwise in half. Set aside.

Now, combine pumpkin, bell pepper, orange, and lime in a juicer and process until juiced. Transfer to serving glasses and sprinkle with some rosemary to taste.

Refrigerate for 15 minutes before serving.

Nutrition information per serving: Kcal: 149, Protein: 4.9g, Carbs: 44.6g, Fats: 0.7g

35.   Spinach Radish Juice

Ingredients:

1 cup of fresh spinach, torn

2 large radishes, chopped

1 cup of cucumber, sliced

1 cup of arugula, torn

¼ tsp turmeric, ground

Preparation:

Wash the spinach thoroughly under cold running water. Slightly drain and torn with hands. Set aside.

Wash the radishes and trim off the green parts. Peel and cut into thin slices. Set aside.

Wash the cucumber and cut into thin slices. Set aside.

Wash the arugula and torn with hands. Set aside.

Now, combine spinach, radish, cucumber, and arugula in a juicer and process until juiced. Transfer to a serving glass and stir in the turmeric.

Refrigerate for 15 minutes before serving.

Nutrition information per serving: Kcal: 53, Protein: 9.4g, Carbs: 15.3g, Fats: 1.1g

36.   Mint Lime Juice

Ingredients:

1 cup of fresh mint

1 large lime, peeled

2 large honeydew melon wedges

1 large yellow apple, cored

2 oz of coconut water

Preparation:

Wash the mint thoroughly under cold running water. Drain and torn with hands. Set aside.

Peel the lime and cut lengthwise in half. Set aside.

Cut the honeydew melon lengthwise in half. Scoop out the seeds using a spoon. Cut two large wedges and peel them. Cut into small chunks and place in a bowl. Wrap the rest of the melon in a plastic foil and refrigerate.

Wash the apple and remove the core. Cut into bite-sized pieces and set aside.

Now, combine mint, lime, honeydew melon, and apple in a juicer. Transfer to serving glasses and stir in the coconut water.

Add some ice and serve immediately.

Nutrition information per serving: Kcal: 228, Protein: 3.4g, Carbs: 65.7g, Fats: 1g

37.   Cantaloupe Juice

Ingredients:

1 cup of cantaloupe, diced

1 cup of baby spinach, torn

1 cup of cranberries

1 cup of parsley, chopped

1 medium-sized cucumber, peeled

1 tbsp of honey, raw

Preparation:

Cut the cantaloupe in half. Scoop out the seeds and flesh. Cut two wedges and peel them. Chop into chunks and set aside. Reserve the rest of the cantaloupe in a refrigerator.

Combine spinach and parsley in a colander and wash under cold running water. Torn with hands and set aside.

Wash the cranberries and set aside.

Wash the cucumber and cut into thick slices. Set aside.

Now, process cantaloupe, baby spinach, cranberries, parsley, and cucumber in a juicer.

Transfer to serving glasses and stir in the honey.

Refrigerate for 30 minutes before serving.

Enjoy!

Nutritional information per serving: Kcal: 197, Protein: 10.2g, Carbs: 58.3g, Fats: 2.2g

38.   Ginger Butternut Squash Juice

Ingredients:

½ cup of butternut squash cubes

2 slices of fresh ginger

1 large red delicious apple, peeled and cored

1 large carrot

1 tbsp of fresh mint, finely chopped

1 large orange, peeled

1 tsp of pure coconut sugar

Preparation:

Run the ingredients through a juicer.

Transfer to a serving glass and stir in one teaspoon of pure coconut sugar.

Serve with ice.

Nutritional information per serving: Kcal: 314, Protein: 5.3g, Carbs: 61g, Fats: 1.2g

39.   Pomegranate Cantaloupe Juice

Ingredients:

1 cup of pomegranate seeds

1 large wedge of cantaloupe

1 small green apple, cored

1 small ginger knob, sliced

1 oz of water

Preparation:

Cut the top of the pomegranate fruit using a sharp paring knife. Slice down to each of the white membranes inside of the fruit. Pop the seeds into a measuring cup and set aside.

Cut the cantaloupe in half. Scrape out the seeds and cut one one large wedge. Peel and chop into small pieces. Wrap the rest in a plastic foil and refrigerate for later.

Wash the apple and cut lengthwise in half. Remove the core and cut into bite-sized pieces. Set aside.

Peel the ginger and cut into small pieces. Set aside.

Now, combine pomegranate, cantaloupe, apple, and ginger in a juicer. Process until well juiced and transfer to a serving glass. Add some water to adjust the bitterness, if needed.

Refrigerate for 10-15 minutes before serving.

Nutrition information per serving: Kcal: 162, Protein: 3.1g, Carbs: 45.3g, Fats: 1.5g

MEALS

1.   Sweet Potato Frittata

Ingredients:

6 large eggs, beaten

1 medium-sized bell pepper, sliced

1 small red onion, finely chopped

1 cup of sweet potatoes, cubed

2 garlic cloves, crushed

¼ cup of Cheddar cheese, grated

1 tbsp of fresh parsley, finely chopped

1 tbsp of extra-virgin olive oil

Preparation:

First, you need to prepare the vegetables. Place the potatoes in a pot of boiling water and cook for 10 minutes, or until fork-tender. Remove from the heat and drain well. Set aside.

Whisk in the eggs, parsley, and cheese in a medium bowl. Mix until well incorporated and set aside.

Now, preheat the oil in a large nonstick frying pan over a medium-high temperature. Add crushed garlic, onion, and pepper and cook for 3-4 minutes, stirring occasionally.

Add the potatoes and cook for another 3 minutes. pour the egg mixture over the vegetables and stir to spread evenly. Cook until eggs are set and remove from the heat.

Serve immediately.

Nutritional information per serving: Kcal: 229, Protein: 12.4g, Carbs: 15.6g, Fats: 13g

2.　　Potato with Garlic

Ingredients:

3 large potatoes, peeled and wedged

3 tbsp of extra-virgin olive oil

4 garlic cloves, minced

1 small onion, finely chopped

1 tbsp of fresh thyme, finely chopped

1 tsp of fresh rosemary, finely chopped

¼ tsp of black pepper, freshly ground

Preparation:

Place the potatoes in a pot of boiling water and cook for 10 minutes, or until tender. Remove from the heat and drain well. Refresh under cold running water and then drain again. Set aside.

Preheat the oil in a small saucepan over a medium-high temperature. Add garlic and onion and cook for 3 minutes. Stir in the thyme, rosemary, and pepper. Cook for 2 minutes more and remove from the heat.

Preheat the grill to a medium-high temperature. Brush the potatoes with oil mixture and grill for 8-10 minutes, or until slightly browned.

Transfer the potatoes to a serving plate and drizzle with the remaining mixture. Top with sour cream and serve immediately.

Nutritional information per serving: Kcal: 383, Protein: 6.1g, Carbs: 48g, Fats: 19.8g

3.   Veal and Peppers in Milk Sauce

Ingredients:

1 lb of lean veal, cut into bite-sized pieces

½ cup of chicken stock, unsalted

2 large red bell peppers, seeded and halved

4 tbsp of milk, low-fat

1 small onion, finely chopped

1 tbsp of olive oil

¼ tsp of black pepper, ground

Preparation:

Preheat the oil in a large saucepan over a medium-high temperature. Add meat chops and cook for 5 minutes, stirring occasionally. Pour the chicken stock and cook for another 5 minutes, until almost all the liquid evaporates. Remove the meat and reserve the saucepan.

Throw in the garlic and onion. Cook until translucent and then add pepper halves. Cook for 2-3 minutes, or until peppers slightly soften. Pour in the milk and cook for 2 minutes. Remove from the heat.

Serve meat with peppers and drizzle with the remaining milk sauce from the saucepan. Serve warm.

Nutritional information per serving: Kcal: 260, Protein: 29g, Carbs: 7g, Fats: 12.6g

4. Orange Peach Smoothie

Ingredients:

2 large peaches, pitted and chopped

1 large orange, peeled

1 cup of milk, low-fat

½ tsp of cherry extract

1 large banana

1 tbsp of sunflower seeds

Preparation:

Wash the peaches and cut in half. Remove the pits and cut into small pieces. Transfer to a food processor.

Peel the orange and divide into wedges. Transfer to a food processor. Peel the banana and cut into chunks. Transfer to a food processor along with milk, cherry extract, and banana. Blend for 2 minutes or until smooth and creamy.

Transfer to serving glasses and top with sunflower seeds. Refrigerate for 15 minutes before serving.

Enjoy!

Nutritional information per serving: Kcal: 157, Protein: 4.9g, Carbs: 31.2g, Fats: 2.6g

5.　　Scrambled Eggs with Mushrooms

Ingredients:

1 cup of button mushrooms, sliced

1 large green bell pepper, sliced

5 large eggs

1 tbsp of scallions

½ tsp of dried oregano, ground

2 tbsp of milk, low-fat

1 tbsp of olive oil

¼ tsp of black pepper, ground

Preparation:

Preheat the oil in a large nonstick skillet over a medium-high temperature. Add mushrooms and bell pepper. Cook for 5 minutes, or until slightly tender. Stir occasionally.

Meanwhile, whisk the eggs with scallions, oregano, milk, and pepper. Pour the mixture into a skillet and fry for 3-5 minutes. Using a wooden spatula, scrape out the eggs from the bottom of the skillet to cook evenly.

Remove from the heat and serve immediately.

Nutritional information per serving: Kcal: 276, Protein: 18.1g, Carbs: 8g, Fats: 20.1g

6.   Warm Carrot Oatmeal

Ingredients:

1 cup of rolled oats

1 cup of milk, low-fat

1 cup of carrots, pre-cooked

¼ tsp of cinnamon, ground

1 tbsp of flaxseeds

1 tbsp of honey

1 tbsp of Brazil nuts, roughly chopped

Preparation:

Wash and peel the carrots. Chop into thin slices and place in a pot of boiling water. Cook for 15 minutes, or until soften. Remove from the heat and drain. Set aside to cool for a while.

Meanwhile, combine oats, milk, cinnamon, and honey in a fire-proof dish. Place it in a microwave for 3 minutes and set aside.

Now, place the carrots in a food processor or a blender. Process until pureed and add it to the oats. Stir all well and reheat in a microwave to the desired temperature.

Sprinkle with nuts and flaxseeds before serving.

Enjoy!

Nutritional information per serving: Kcal: 322, Protein: 11.2g, Carbs: 49.6g, Fats: 9.6g

7. Trout with Pasta

Ingredients:

1 lb of trout fillets

8 oz of pasta

1 cup of tomato sauce

2 tbsp of extra-virgin olive oil

1 tbsp of balsamic vinegar

2 garlic cloves, minced

1 tsp of Italian seasoning mix

¼ tsp of dried oregano, ground

1 tbsp of fresh parsley, finely chopped

1 tbsp of lemon juice, freshly squeezed

Preparation:

Prepare the pasta using package instructions. Drain the pasta and set aside.

Preheat the oil in a large skillet over a medium-high temperature. Add garlic and saute for 2-3 minutes, or until translucent. Now, add fish fillets and sprinkle with balsamic vinegar, Italian seasoning mix, oregano, and lemon juice. Cook the fillets for 5 minutes on both sides, or until set. Remove from the heat.

Now, transfer pasta to serving plates and top with fish fillets. Sprinkle with parsley and serve immediately.

Nutritional information per serving: Kcal: 458, Protein: 37.6g, Carbs: 35.1g, Fats: 18.1g

8.   Strawberry Spinach Salad

Ingredients:

10 oz of fresh spinach, roughly chopped

1 cup of strawberries, chopped

1 medium-sized cucumber, sliced

2 tbsp of almonds, roughly chopped

2 tbsp of orange juice, freshly juiced

1 tbsp of extra-virgin olive oil

1 tbsp of honey

Preparation:

Combine almonds, orange juice, oil, and honey in a medium bowl. Stir well and set aside.

Wash the spinach thoroughly under cold running water. Drain and roughly chop it. Set aside.

Wash the strawberries and cut into bite-sized pieces. Set aside.

Wash the cucumber and chop it into thin slices. Set aside.

Now, combine spinach, strawberries, and cucumber in a salad bowl. Stir well and then drizzle with previously prepared sauce. Toss well to coat and refrigerate for 20 minutes before serving.

Enjoy!

Nutritional information per serving: Kcal: 141, Protein: 4.6g, Carbs: 18.4g, Fats: 7.3g

9.   Kidney Beans Stew

Ingredients:

10 oz of kidney beans, soaked overnight

1 cup of canned tomatoes, diced

1 tbsp of tomato paste

1 medium-sized bell pepper

1 tbsp of olive oil

1 small onion, finely chopped

2 garlic cloves, crushed

1 medium-sized potato, chopped

2 cups of water

Preparation:

Soak the beans overnight. Drain well and rinse under cold running water. Drain again and set aside.

Place the beans in a deep pot and add 3 cups of water. Bring it to a boil and continue to cook for 15 minutes. Remove from the heat, drain, and set aside.

Peel the potato and cut into small chunks. Place it in a pot of boiling water and cook for 5 minutes. Remove from the heat and drain well. Set aside.

Preheat the oil in a heavy-bottomed pot over a medium-high temperature. Add garlic and onions and stir-fry for 3-4 minutes, or until translucent.

Now, add all other ingredients and bring it to a boil. Reduce the heat to low and cover with a lid. Cook for 30 minutes and remove from the heat.

Serve warm.

Nutritional information per serving: Kcal: 227, Protein: 12.1g, Carbs: 39.8g, Fats: 3g

10.   Tuna Steaks with Cherry Tomatoes

Ingredients:

2 lbs of tuna steaks

3 garlic cloves, crushed

4 tbsp of extra-virgin olive oil

1 tsp of fresh coriander, finely chopped

1 tbsp of fresh rosemary, finely chopped

2 tbsp of lemon juice, freshly squeezed

¼ tsp of black pepper, freshly ground

1 cup of cherry tomatoes, halved

Preparation:

Wash the tuna steaks under cold running water and pat dry with a kitchen paper.

In a small bowl, combine oil, garlic, coriander, rosemary, lemon juice, and pepper. Stir well until well incorporated. Spread this mixture over the tuna steaks.

Preheat the grill to a medium-high temperature. Grill the steaks for about 5-7 minutes on both sides, or until desired doneness. Serve steaks with fresh cherry tomatoes.

Nutritional information per serving: Kcal: 369, Protein: 45.7g, Carbs: 2.2g, Fats: 19g

11.   Creamy Blackberry Salad

Ingredients:

1 cup of fresh blackberries

1 cup of strawberries, halved

1 large Granny Smith's apple, cut into bite-sized pieces

1 large cucumber, sliced

1 cup of sour cream, low-fat

1 tbsp of honey, raw

2 tbsp of olive oil

2 tbsp of almonds, roughly chopped

1 tbsp of walnuts, roughly chopped

Preparation:

Wash and prepare the fruits and vegetables.

Combine sour cream, almonds, walnuts, honey, and oil in a medium bowl. Set aside to allow flavors to meld.

Now, combine blackberries, strawberries, apple, and cucumber in a large salad bowl. Add sour cream mixture and stir well to coat all the ingredients.

Refrigerate for 15 minutes before serving and enjoy!

Nutritional information per serving: Kcal: 296, Protein: 4.3g, Carbs: 24.3g, Fats: 22.2g

12.   Grilled Salmon with Potatoes

Ingredients:

2 lbs of salmon fillets

2 large potatoes, cut into bite-sized pieces

3 tbsp of lemon juice, freshly squeezed

3 garlic cloves, crushed

1 tbsp of fresh basil, finely chopped

1 tbsp of fresh rosemary, finely chopped

4 tbsp of olive oil

¼ tsp of black pepper, ground

Preparation:

Wash the fillets under cold running water and pat dry with a kitchen paper. Set aside.

Peel the potatoes and cut into bite-sized pieces. Place the potatoes in a pot of boiling water and cook for 15 minutes, or until fork-tender. Remove from the heat and drain. Set aside.

In a large bowl, combine olive oil, garlic, rosemary, basil, lemon juice, and pepper. Stir well to combine and set aside.

Preheat the grill to a medium-high temperature. Gently brush the fillets with sauce and place on a grill.

Grill for 2-3 minutes on each side, or until doneness. Remove from the heat and transfer to a serving plate. Add potatoes and drizzle with the remaining sauce. Serve immediately.

Nutritional information per serving: Kcal: 388, Protein: 31.6g, Carbs: 20.4g, Fats: 20.9g

13.   Creamy Leek Soup

Ingredients:

1 cup of leeks, chopped

1 medium-sized potato

1 large carrot, chopped

1 cup of chicken stock, unsalted

1 cup of milk, low-fat

1 cup of spinach, finely chopped

1 tbsp of parsley, finely chopped

¼ tsp of black pepper, ground

Preparation:

Wash and prepare the vegetables. Place the leeks, spinach, and celery in a pot of boiling water. Cook for 3 minutes and remove from the heat. Drain well and set aside.

Place the potato in a pot of boiling water and cook for 5 minutes, or until slightly tender. Remove from the heat and drain well. Set aside.

Now, combine leeks, potato, carrot, and spinach in a heavy-bottomed pot. Pour the chicken stock and milk. Sprinkle with pepper and parsley. Bring it to a boil and then reduce the heat to low. Simmer for 15 minutes and remove from the heat.

Serve warm.

Nutritional information per serving: Kcal: 89, Protein: 4g, Carbs: 17.8g, Fats: 0.3g

14.   Banana Almond Smoothie

Ingredients:

1 large banana, chopped

2 tbsp of almonds

1 cup of Greek yogurt

1 small carrot, sliced

1 tsp of vanilla extract

Preparation:

Peel the banana and chop into small chunks. Set aside.

Peel the carrots and cut into thin slices. Set aside.

Now, combine banana, carrots, almonds, yogurt, and vanilla extract in a food processor or a blender. Blend until nicely smooth and transfer to serving glasses. Sprinkle with some extra almonds and add some ice before serving.

Enjoy!

Nutritional information per serving: Kcal: 202, Protein: 14.3g, Carbs: 24.4g, Fats: 5.6g

15.   Shiitake Collard Greens

Ingredients:

1 cup of Shiitake mushrooms, chopped

2 cups of collard greens, chopped

2 garlic cloves, minced

2 tbsp of extra-virgin olive oil

2 tbsp of lemon juice, freshly squeezed

1 tbsp of Dijon mustard

¼ tsp of black pepper

½ cup of chicken broth, unsalted

Preparation:

In a medium bowl, combine 1 tablespoon of olive oil, garlic, lemon juice, mustard, and pepper. Stir until well incorporated and set aside.

Preheat the remaining oil in a large nonstick saucepan over a medium-high temperature. Add mushrooms and cook for 10 minutes. Transfer mushrooms to a bowl and reserve the pan.

Pour the chicken broth into the pan and add garlic. Bring it to a boil and then add collard greens. Cook for 5 minutes then reduce the heat. Add mushrooms and cook for another 2 minutes. Remove from the heat and transfer to a serving plate. Drizzle with previously made sauce and serve immediately.

Nutritional information per serving: Kcal: 185, Protein: 4g, Carbs: 14.5g, Fats: 14g

16.   Turkey Breasts with Zucchini

Ingredients:

1 lb of turkey breasts, skinless and boneless

1 large zucchini, peeled and chopped

3 garlic cloves, minced

1 small onion, finely chopped

3 tbsp of extra-virgin olive oil

¼ tsp of black pepper, ground

Preparation:

Peel the zucchinis and cut in half. Scrape out the seeds and chop into small chunks. Place in a pot of boiling water and cook for 5 minutes, or until tender. Set aside.

Now, preheat the oil in a large frying pan over a medium-high temperature. Add garlic and onions and cook for 3 minutes, or until translucent. Add turkey breasts and cook for 10 minutes more, stirring occasionally. Throw in the zucchinis and sprinkle with some pepper. Cook for 3 minutes more and remove from the heat.

Serve immediately.

Nutritional information per serving: Kcal: 232, Protein: 20.7g, Carbs: 9.9g, Fats: 12.6g

17.   Lean Shrimp Stew with Brussels Sprouts

Ingredients:

1 lb of large shrimps, cleaned and deveined

7 oz of Brussels sprouts, trimmed

5 oz of okra

2 small carrots, sliced

3 oz of baby corn

2 cups of chicken broth

2 large tomatoes, diced

2 tbsp of tomato paste

½ tsp of chili pepper, ground

¼ tsp of black pepper, freshly ground

½ cup of olive oil

1 tbsp of balsamic vinegar

1 tbsp of fresh rosemary, finely chopped

1 small celery stalk, for decoration

2 tbsp of sour cream

Preparation:

Wash the shrimps under cold running water and pat dry with a kitchen paper. Set aside.

Combine 3 tablespoons of olive oil, balsamic vinegar, rosemary, and pepper in a large bowl. Stir well and place the shrimps into the bowl. Toss well to coat and refrigerate for 20 minutes to allow flavors to meld into the shrimps.

Meanwhile, wash and prepare the vegetables. Trim off the outer layers of the Brussels sprouts and slice the carrots.

Now, preheat the remaining oil in a heavy-bottomed pot over a medium-high temperature. Add Brussels sprouts, okra, carrots and celery. Saute for 5 minutes. Add tomatoes, tomato paste, and chili. Sprinkle with some pepper and stir well to combine. Cook for 3 minutes more.

Drain the shrimps and add to the pot. Pour about 2 cups of water and give it a good stir. Reduce the heat to low and cook for 15 minutes. Add corn and cook for 3 minutes more. Remove from the heat and transfer to a serving plate. Top with sour cream and drizzle little bit with a shrimp marinade.

Nutrition information per serving: Kcal: 193, Protein: 15.7g, Carbs: 20.1g, Fats: 7.2g

18.   Sweet Potato Tuna

Ingredients:

1 lb of tuna fillets

4 tbsp of olive oil

1 tbsp of balsamic vinegar

2 tbsp of lemon juice

1 tbsp of toasted almonds

¼ tsp of black pepper, ground

1 medium-sized sweet potato

Preparation:

In a medium bowl, combine oil, vinegar, lemon juice, almond, and pepper. Mix well and set aside to allow flavors to blend.

Peel the potato and cut into small chunks. Place it in a pot of boiling water. Cook for 20 minutes, or until fork-tender. Remove from the heat and set aside.

Preheat the electric grill to a medium-high temperature. Brush the tuna fillets with marinade and grill for about 2-3 minutes on each side.

Transfer to a serving plate and serve with potatoes. Drizzle all with marinade and serve immediately.

Nutrition information per serving: Kcal: 491, Protein: 41.4g, Carbs: 8.7g, Fats: 32g

19. Pineapple Salad

Ingredients:

1 cup of pineapple chunks

1 large mango, chopped

1 cup of Iceberg lettuce, torn

1 cup of fresh spinach, torn

1 cup of blueberries

4 tbsp of orange juice, freshly juiced

2 tbsp of lemon juice

1 tbsp of honey

2 tbsp of walnuts, roughly chopped

Preparation:

Combine orange juice, lemon juice, honey, and walnuts in a small bowl. Mix until well incorporated and set aside to allow flavors to mingle. Set aside.

Wash and prepare the fruits and vegetables.

Peel and cut the pineapple and mango into small chunks and set aside.

In a large colander, combine lettuce and spinach and wash under cold running water. Torn with hands and set aside.

Wash the blueberries and combine along with pineapple, mango, lettuce, and spinach in a large salad bowl. Drizzle with marinade and refrigerate for 15 minutes before serving.

Enjoy!

Nutrition information per serving: Kcal: 192, Protein: 3.5g, Carbs: 40.5g, Fats: 3.9g

20.   Creamy Quinoa with Dates

Ingredients:

1 cup of quinoa, pre-cooked

¼ cup of dates, chopped

1 tbsp of cashews, roughly chopped

1 tsp of pumpkin seeds

¼ tsp of cinnamon, ground

1 cup of milk, low-fat

1 tbsp of honey

Preparation:

Place the quinoa in a deep pot. Add 3 cups of water and bring it to a boil. Reduce the heat to low and cook for 15 minutes. Remove from the heat and drain. Stir once and set aside.

Now, combine quinoa, dates, cinnamon, cashews, milk, and honey in a medium bowl. Stir well to combine and transfer to serving dishes.

Top with pumpkin seeds and serve immediately.

Nutrition information per serving: Kcal: 192, Protein: 3.5g, Carbs: 40.5g, Fats: 3.9g

21.   Cherry Muffins

Ingredients:

2 cups of buckwheat flour

7 oz of cherries, pitted

3 tsp of baking powder

1 cup of milk, low-fat

6 tbsp of cream cheese, low-fat

1 tbsp of liquid honey

2 large eggs

1 large pear, peeled, cored, and finely chopped

Preparation:

Preheat the oven to 400°F.

In a medium bowl, combine flour and baking powder. Stir well and set aside.

Wash the cherries and pear. Cut the cherries in half and remove the pits. Peel the pear and remove the core. Cut into bite-sized pieces and set aside.

Now, combine pear, cherries, eggs, milk, and honey in a large bowl. Stir well to combine and pour this mixture over a flour mixture. Stir well until you get nice dough.

Grease muffin molds with some oil and spoon the mixture evenly. Top with each muffin with cream cheese.

Place it in the oven and bake for 25 minutes, or until set. Remove from the oven and set aside to cool.

Serve warm.

Nutritional information per serving: Kcal: 278, Protein: 9.4g, Carbs: 47.5g, Fats: 7.3g

22.   Strawberry Banana Smoothie

Ingredients:

1 cup of strawberries

1 large banana

1 cup of milk, low-fat

1 tbsp pumpkin seeds

1 tsp of vanilla extract

Preparation:

Wash the strawberries under cold running water and cut in half. transfer to a food processor.

Peel the banana and cut into chunks. Add it to the food processor along with milk and vanilla extract. Blend for 2 minutes or until smooth and creamy.

Transfer to serving glasses and top with pumpkin seeds. Refrigerate for 15 minutes, or add some ice before serving.

Enjoy!

Nutritional information per serving: Kcal: 116, Protein: 4.2g, Carbs: 18.7g, Fats: 3.3g

23.   Celery Nutmeg Omelet

Ingredients:

1 cup of celery, finely chopped

1 large red onion, chopped

¼ tsp of nutmeg, ground

6 large eggs

1 tbsp of milk, low-fat

1 tbsp of olive oil

Preparation:

In a medium bowl, whisk together eggs with nutmeg, and milk. Set aside.

Wash and prepare the celery and onion. Set aside.

Preheat the oil in a large nonstick frying pan over a medium-high temperature. Add onion and stir-fry for 2 minutes. Now, add celery and continue to cook for 2 more minutes.

Pour the egg mixture into the pan and cook for 3-4 minutes, or until eggs are set. Fold the omelet and remove from the pan.

Serve immediately.

Nutritional information per serving: Kcal: 212, Protein: 13.5g, Carbs: 6.8g, Fats: 14.9g

24.   Creamy Leek Artichoke Soup

Ingredients:

1 lb of leeks, chopped

1 medium-sized onion

1 cup of artichoke, chopped

1 tbsp of olive oil

1 tbsp of fresh parsley, finely chopped

3 cups of vegetable broth, unsalted

2 tbsp of lemon juice, freshly squeezed

¼ tsp of black pepper, ground

Preparation:

Preheat the oil in a heavy-bottomed pot over a medium-high temperature. Add onions and stir-fry for about 2-3 minutes.

Now, add leeks, artichokes, and lemon juice. Stir well and cook for 2 minutes. Add vegetable broth and sprinkle with some pepper to taste. Stir again and cook for 15 minutes. Remove from the heat.

Using a large colander, drain all the liquid to another pot. Transfer the vegetables to a food processor and blend well until smooth. Return to a pot with broth. Heat it up for 4-5 minutes and serve immediately.

Nutritional information per serving: Kcal: 102, Protein: 4.5g, Carbs: 15.4g, Fats: 4.5g

25.   Baked Veal with Carrots

Ingredients:

1 lb of lean veal, cut into bite-sized pieces

1 tbsp of buckwheat flour

2 tbsp of olive oil

1 medium-sized carrot, chopped

1 cup of tomato sauce

1 tbsp of balsamic vinegar

¼ tsp of black pepper, freshly ground

1 tbsp of fresh thyme, finely chopped

Preparation:

Preheat the oven to 400°F.

Combine flour, vinegar, tomato sauce, vinegar, and one tablespoon of olive oil. Stir well until combined and set aside.

Grease a large baking sheet with oil. Spread the meat chops evenly onto it. Sprinkle with pepper, and thyme, and squeeze with your hands to rub in the spices. Tuck in the carrot slices between the meat chops and place it in the oven.

Bake for about 15 minutes and then add the tomato sauce mixture. Spread evenly and continue to bake for 5 more minutes. Remove from the oven and serve warm.

Nutritional information per serving: Kcal: 102, Protein: 4.5g, Carbs: 15.4g, Fats: 4.5g

26.   Apricot Oatmeal with Flaxseeds

Ingredients:

4 medium-sized apricots, chopped

1 cup of milk, low-fat

1 tbsp of honey

1 tbsp of flaxseeds

1 cup of oatmeal

Preparation:

Wash the apricots and cut in half. Remove the pits and cut into small pieces. Transfer to a deep pot and add 2 cups of water. Bring it to a boil and cook for 2 minutes. Remove from the heat and drain. Set aside to cool for a while.

Combine oatmeal, milk, honey, and flaxseeds. Stir well and place it in a microwave. Heat it up for 1 minute and then stir in the apricots.

Serve immediately.

Nutritional information per serving: Kcal: 300, Protein: 11g, Carbs: 51g, Fats: 6.7g

27.   Turkey Breasts with Arugula Cream

Ingredients:

1 lb of turkey breasts, skinless and boneless

1 cup of fresh arugula, chopped

1 large tomato, diced

3 tbsp of olive oil

2 tbsp of lemon juice, freshly squeezed

½ tsp of black pepper, freshly ground

1 tsp of dried thyme, ground

Preparation:

In a large bowl, combine arugula, tomato, lemon juice, and pepper. Stir well to combine and transfer to a blender. Process until creamy and set aside.

Preheat the oil in a large nonstick skillet over a medium-high temperature. Add turkey breasts and sprinkle with thyme. Cook for 4-5 minutes on each side, or until desired doneness.

Transfer to a serving plate and pour over the arugula cream. Serve with some lemon wedges or sprinkle with lemon zest. However, this is optional.

Enjoy!

Nutritional information per serving: Kcal: 294, Protein: 26.7g, Carbs: 9.6g, Fats: 16.8g

28. Sweet Potato Pasta

Ingredients:

1 lb of whole-grain penne pasta

2 large tomatoes, diced

3 tbsp of tomato paste

2 medium-sized sweet potatoes, chopped

2 tbsp of sour cream

1 tbsp of balsamic vinegar

1 tsp of dried oregano

½ tsp of Italian seasoning mix

1 tbsp of fresh parsley, finely chopped

Preparation:

Cook the pasta using package instructions. Remove from the heat and drain well. Set aside.

Peel the potatoes and chop into small pieces. Place in a pot of boiling water and cook until fork-tender. Remove from the heat and drain well. Set aside to cool for a while.

Preheat the oil in a large skillet over a medium-high temperature. Add tomatoes, tomato paste, oregano, and Italian seasoning mix. Stir well and cook for 2 minutes. Add sweet potatoes and sour cream. Cook for 2 minutes more and remove from the heat.

Transfer the pasta to serving plates and top with tomato sauce. Sprinkle with some fresh parsley and serve immediately.

Nutritional information per serving: Kcal: 304, Protein: 10.4g, Carbs: 59.6g, Fats: 2.9g

29. Bell Pepper Polenta

Ingredients:

1 cup of cornstarch

3 cups of water

1 small onion, finely chopped

1 medium-sized red bell pepper, chopped

1 medium-sized green bell pepper, chopped

1 tbsp of vegetable oil

½ cup of sour cream, low-fat

Preparation:

Pour the water in a deep pot. Bring it to a boil and then gently stir in the cornstarch. Cook for 20 minutes on medium temperature. Stir constantly until mixture nicely thickens. Remove from the heat and set aside.

Preheat the oil in a medium nonstick skillet over a medium-high temperature. Add onion and stir-fry until translucent. Now, add peppers and cook for 5 minutes, or until peppers soften. Remove from the heat and set aside.

Transfer the polenta to serving plates and spoon the peppers and onion. Top with sour cream and serve immediately.

Nutritional information per serving: Kcal: 304, Protein: 10.4g, Carbs: 59.6g, Fats: 2.9g

30. Green Bean Brussels Sprout Stew

Ingredients:

1 cup of green beans, chopped

1 cup of Brussel sprouts, chopped

2 cups of vegetable broth

1 large carrot, chopped

1 cup of sweet potatoes, chopped

1 large tomato, diced

2 tbsp of tomato paste

1 tsp of cayenne pepper, ground

¼ tsp of black pepper, ground

2 tbsp of olive oil

1 tsp of dried thyme, ground

Preparation:

Place the sweet potatoes in a pot of boiling water. Cook for 10 minutes and then remove from the heat. Drain and set aside.

Preheat the oil in a heavy-bottomed pot over a medium-high temperature. Add Brussels sprouts, carrots, and green beans. Cook for 5 minutes, stirring occasionally. Now, pour the broth and add tomato. Stir and cook for 10 minutes. Reduce the heat to low.

Stir in the tomato paste and sprinkle with pepper, cayenne pepper, and thyme.

Cook for 5 minutes more and remove from the heat.

Enjoy!

Nutritional information per serving: Kcal: 133, Protein: 4.2g, Carbs: 16.3g, Fats: 6.5g

31.   Trout with Potato Puree

Ingredients:

1 lb of trout fillets

1 cup of sweet potatoes, chopped

½ cup of spring onions, finely chopped

3 tbsp of olive oil

2 tbsp of lemon juice, freshly squeezed

3 garlic cloves, crushed

½ tsp of black pepper, ground

1 tbsp of fresh rosemary, finely chopped

1 tsp of balsamic vinegar

Preparation:

Place chopped potatoes in a pot of boiling water and cook for 10 minutes. Remove from the heat and drain well. Set aside.

In a small bowl, combine olive oil, lemon juice, garlic, pepper, and rosemary. Stir well to combine and set aside.

Preheat the grill to a medium-high temperature. Brush the fillets with marinade and grill for 3-4 minutes on each side. Brush occasionally when dried out. Transfer the fillets to a bowl and cover with a lid. Set aside.

Now, place the potatoes and remaining marinade into a food processor. Blend until smooth and set aside.

Serve the fillets with potato puree.

Nutritional information per serving: Kcal: 363, Protein: 31.3g, Carbs: 13g, Fats: 20.4g

32. Watermelon Kale Smoothie

Ingredients:

1 cup of fresh kale, chopped

1 cup of watermelon chunks

1 tsp of turmeric, ground

1 tbsp of liquid honey

½ cup of sour cream, low-fat

Preparation:

Wash the kale thoroughly under cold running water. Drain and roughly chop it. Set aside.

Peel the watermelon lengthwise in half. Cut one large wedge and peel it. Chop into chunks and discard the seeds. Set aside.

Now, combine kale, watermelon, turmeric, honey, and sour cream in a food processor or a blender. Process until smooth and creamy. Transfer to serving glasses and refrigerate for 15 minutes before serving.

Enjoy!

Nutritional information per serving: Kcal: 198, Protein: 3.4g, Carbs: 21g, Fats: 12.3g

33.   Kiwi Raspberry Salad

Ingredients:

2 large kiwis, chopped

1 cup of raspberries

1 cup of watermelon, chopped

1 large peach, chopped

2 tbsp of lemon juice, freshly squeezed

2 tbsp of orange juice, freshly squeezed

2 tbsp of walnuts, roughly chopped

Preparation:

In a small bowl, combine lemon juice, orange juice, and walnuts. Stir and set aside.

Wash the peach and cut in half. Remove the pit and cut into bite-sized pieces. Wash the raspberries under cold running water. Peel the kiwis and cut lengthwise in half.

Cut the watermelon in half. Cut one large wedge and peel it. Discard the seeds and fill the measuring cup. Wrap the rest in a plastic foil and refrigerate.

Now, combine kiwis, raspberries, watermelon, and peach in a large salad bowl. Drizzle with the dressing and toss well to combine all the ingredients.

Refrigerate for 15 minutes before serving.

Nutritional information per serving: Kcal: 126, Protein: 3.2g, Carbs: 22.6g, Fats: 3.9g

34.   Chicken with Brown Rice

Ingredients:

1 lb of chicken breasts, skinless and boneless

1 cup of brown rice

¼ cup of spring onions, finely chopped

1 small carrot, sliced

2 tbsp of olive oil

¼ tsp of turmeric, ground

¼ tsp of black pepper, ground

¼ tsp of dried oregano, ground

Preparation:

Place the rice in a heavy-bottomed pot. Add 3 cups of water and bring it to a boil. Cook for 15 minutes, then reduce the heat to low. Stir in the turmeric and cook for 2 minutes more. Remove from the heat. Stir in the green onions and set aside.

Preheat the oil in a large skillet over a medium-high temperature. Add onions and carrot and cook for 3-4 minutes.

Now, add meat and sprinkle with some pepper, and oregano. Cook for about 4-5 minutes or until desired doneness. Remove from the heat and transfer to a serving plate.

Serve the chicken breasts with rice and enjoy.

Nutritional information per serving: Kcal: 456, Protein: 36.6g, Carbs: 38.1g, Fats: 16.7g

35. Green Muffins

Ingredients:

2 cups of buckwheat flour

¼ cup of spinach

1 tbsp of sour cream, low-fat

1 tbsp of baking powder

1 cup of milk, low-fat

2 large eggs

Preparation:

Preheat the oven to 300°F.

In a large bowl, combine flour and baking powder. Set aside.

In a separate bowl, combine eggs, sour cream, and milk. Whisk well and set aside.

Using a hand electric mixer, gently stir in the egg mixture into flour mixture. Finally, add spinach and mix until you get the nice smooth dough.

Spoon the muffins into muffin molds. Place it in the oven and bake for about 20-25 minutes, or until set.

Serve warm.

Nutritional information per serving: Kcal: 185, Protein: 8.6g, Carbs: 31.7g, Fats: 4.2g

36. Tomato Eggplant Stew

Ingredients:

2 large tomatoes, peeled and diced

1 small eggplant, chopped

1 medium-sized red bell pepper, chopped

1 cup of sweet potatoes, chopped

2 garlic cloves, crushed

3 tbsp of olive oil

½ tsp of black pepper, ground

1 tsp of salt

Preparation:

Peel the eggplants and chop into small chunks. Place them in a large bowl and generously sprinkle with salt. Set aside for 15 minutes to get rid of the bitterness of the eggplant. Rinse well and pat dry with a kitchen paper. Set aside.

Wash, peel, and chop other vegetables. Rinse well the eggplants and place in a crock pot along with other vegetables. Sprinkle with pepper and pour water enough to cover all ingredients.

Cover with a lid and cook for 2 hours on low temperature, stirring occasionally.

Nutritional information per serving: Kcal: 153, Protein: 2.3g, Carbs: 18.9g, Fats: 8.8g

37. Marinated Mackerel Fillets

Ingredients:

1 lb of mackerel fillets

4 garlic cloves, crushed

2 tbsp of fresh parsley, finely chopped

½ cup of olive oil

2 tbsp of lemon juice, freshly squeezed

¼ tsp of black pepper, freshly ground

1 tbsp of fresh rosemary, finely chopped

1 tsp of balsamic vinegar

Preparation:

In a large bowl, combine garlic, oil, lemon, pepper, rosemary, and vinegar. Mix well and soak the fillets in this marinade. Cover with a plastic foil and refrigerate for about 30 minutes.

Preheat the grill to a medium-high temperature. Drain the fillets and reserve the marinade. Grill for 4-5 minutes on each side, or until desired doneness.

Serve fish with some steamed or broiled vegetables.

Nutritional information per serving: Kcal: 490, Protein: 36.5g, Carbs: 2.5g, Fats: 36.6g

38. Green Cream Soup

Ingredients:

1 cup of fresh broccoli, chopped

1 cup of cauliflower, chopped

4 tbsp of fresh parsley, finely chopped

¼ tsp of chili pepper, ground

1 tsp of dried thyme, ground

½ cup of milk, low-fat

Preparation:

Place broccoli and cauliflower in a heavy-bottomed pot. Add enough water to cover all ingredients and bring it to a boil. Cook for 5 minutes, or until tender. Remove from the heat and drain well. Set aside to cool for a while.

Transfer cooked broccoli and cauliflower to a blender. Add ½ cup of water and sprinkle with chili pepper. Process until pureed and transfer to a clean heavy-bottomed pot.

Add 2 cups of water and sprinkle with finely chopped parsley. Bring it to a boil and reduce the heat to low. Cook for 2 minutes. Add milk and give it a good stir. Cook until heated trough.

Serve warm.

Nutritional information per serving: Kcal: 490, Protein: 36.5g, Carbs: 2.5g, Fats: 36.6g

39.   Fresh Mediterranean Salad

Ingredients:

2 large tomatoes, chopped

1 cup of Romaine lettuce, roughly chopped

1 large green bell pepper, sliced

1 small red onion, sliced

1 small cucumber, sliced

1 tbsp of balsamic vinegar

3 tbsp of extra-virgin olive oil

1 tbsp of fresh parsley, finely chopped

1 tsp of Italian seasoning mix

Preparation:

Wash the tomatoes and place them in a large salad bowl. Cut into bite-sized pieces.

Wash the lettuce thoroughly under cold running water and drain. Roughly chop it and add to the bowl.

Wash the green bell pepper and cut in half. Remove the seeds, slice, and add it to the bowl.

Peel the onions and thinly slice. Add it to the bowl and set aside.

Wash the cucumber and cut into thin slices and add it to the bowl.

Now, combine balsamic vinegar, olive oil, parsley, and Italian seasoning mix. Stir well to mix and pour over the salad. Toss gently to coat all the ingredients.

Refrigerate for 15 minutes before serving and enjoy.

Nutritional information per serving: Kcal: 238, Protein: 1.9g, Carbs: 10.7g, Fats: 10.9g

40. Grilled Veal with Avocado and Mushrooms

Ingredients:

1 lb of lean veal, cut into bite-sized pieces

1 cup of cremini mushrooms, chopped

1 cup of avocado, peeled and chopped

1 cup of lamb's lettuce

1 medium-sized tomato, chopped

1 tsp of dried thyme, ground

¼ tsp of black pepper, ground

3 tbsp of olive oil

Preparation:

Wash the meat thoroughly and pat dry with a kitchen paper. Cut into bite-sized pieces and set aside.

Preheat the oil in a large nonstick saucepan over a medium-high temperature. Add meat and sprinkle with some pepper. Cook for about 5 minutes and then add mushrooms. Sprinkle all with thyme and cook for 7-10 more minutes, or until desired doneness. Remove from the heat and set aside.

Now, combine avocado, tomato, and lettuce on a serving plate. Add meat and mushrooms and serve immediately.

Nutritional information per serving: Kcal: 373, Protein: 29.1g, Carbs: 5.7g, Fats: 26.3g

41.   Spinach Carrot Salad

Ingredients:

2 large carrots, sliced

½ cup of fresh spinach, torn

1 large tomato, chopped

2 oz of blueberries

4 tbsp of lemon juice, freshly squeezed

2 tbsp of orange juice, freshly squeezed

¼ tsp of cumin, ground

1 tsp of yellow mustard

Preparation:

In a small bowl, combine lemon juice, orange juice, cumin, and yellow mustard. Stir well to mix and set aside.

In a large salad bowl, combine carrots, spinach, tomato, and blueberries. Stir well once, then drizzle with marinade and then give it a good final stir.

Refrigerate for 10 minutes before serving.

Enjoy!

Nutritional information per serving: Kcal: 81, Protein: 2.3g, Carbs: 17.5g, Fats: 0.7g

42.   Walnut Oatmeal

Ingredients:

1 tbsp of walnuts, roughly chopped

1 cup of oatmeal

1 cup of water

1 tbsp of honey

¼ cup of dates, chopped

½ cup of sour cream, low-fat

Preparation:

Combine water and oatmeal in a small pot over a medium-high temperature. Bring it to a boil and cook for 2 minutes. Remove from the heat and set aside to cool completely.

Combine walnuts, dates, honey, and sour cream in a bowl. Stir in the cooked oatmeal and transfer to serving bowls.

Enjoy!

Nutritional information per serving: Kcal: 397, Protein: 8.7g, Carbs: 55.9g, Fats: 17.1g

43.   Pomegranate Almond Smoothie

Ingredients:

1 medium-sized pomegranate

1 cup of yogurt, low-fat

2 tbsp of lemon juice, freshly squeezed

1 tbsp of honey

1 tbsp of almonds, roughly chopped

Preparation:

Using a sharp knife, cut the top of the pomegranate fruit. Slice down to each of the white membranes inside of the fruit. Pop the seeds into a cup and then transfer to a food processor.

Add yogurt, lemon juice, and honey. Blend until nicely smooth and transfer to serving glasses. Top with almonds and refrigerate for 20 minutes before serving.

Enjoy!

Nutritional information per serving: Kcal: 190, Protein: 8.3g, Carbs: 31.2g, Fats: 3.1g

44.   Chicken Scrambled Eggs

Ingredients:

10 oz of chicken fillets

4 large eggs

1 small red onion, finely chopped

1 medium-sized red bell pepper, chopped

2 tbsp of olive oil

1 tbsp of fresh parsley, finely chopped

1 tsp of dried thyme, ground

Preparation:

In a medium bowl, whisk the eggs, and parsley. Set aside.

Preheat the oil in a large frying pan over a medium-high temperature. Add onions and pepper and cook for 3 minutes, or until vegetables soften. Now, add chicken and cook for 5 minutes, stirring occasionally.

Pour the egg mixture and spread evenly. Cook for about 3-4 minutes, or until eggs are set.

Serve immediately.

Nutritional information per serving: Kcal: 378, Protein: 36.5g, Carbs: 6g, Fats: 23.1g

45. Beans Spread

Ingredients:

1 lb of kidney beans, pre-cooked

1 cup of sweet corn

2 large tomatoes, diced

4 tbsp of tomato paste

½ tsp of dried oregano, ground

3 tbsp of olive oil

¼ tsp of black pepper, ground

Preparation:

Soak the beans overnight. Rinse and drain well and then place in a deep pot. Add about 6 cups of water and bring it to a boil. Reduce the heat to low and cook for 1 hour. Remove from the heat and drain well. Set aside.

Now, preheat the oil in a large skillet over a medium-high temperature. Add tomatoes, tomato paste and about ½ cup of water. Sprinkle with some pepper and oregano to taste and stir well. Cook for 5 minutes, stirring constantly.

Place the beans in a food processor and add about 2 tablespoons of tomato mixture and 2 tablespoons of water. Blend until well incorporated. Transfer the beans to a skillet with potatoes and stir all well. Add corn and cook for 5 more minutes, stirring constantly.

Remove from the heat and set aside to cool completely. Refrigerate for 30 minutes before serving.

Nutritional information per serving: Kcal: 268, Protein: 14.2g, Carbs: 41.8g, Fats: 6.2g

46.   Sweet Potato with Collard Greens

Ingredients:

1 cup of sweet potato, chopped

1 cup of collard greens, chopped

1 large carrot, sliced

1 small onion, finely chopped

2 garlic cloves, crushed

2 tablespoon of olive oil

Preparation:

Wash the collard thoroughly under cold running water. Roughly chop it and set aside.

Peel the sweet potatoes and cut into bite-sized pieces. Fill the measuring cup and reserve the rest for some other recipe. Now, place the potatoes in a pot of boiling water and cook for 15 minutes, or until tender. Remove from the heat and drain.

Preheat the oil in a large skillet over a medium-high temperature. Add garlic, carrot, and onion and cook for 3 minutes, or until carrot slightly tender. Add potatoes and collard greens and cook for 5 more minutes. Remove from the heat and serve immediately.

Enjoy!

Nutritional information per serving: Kcal: 250, Protein: 3.4g, Carbs: 29.7g, Fats: 14.4g

ADDITIONAL TITLES FROM THIS AUTHOR

70 Effective Meal Recipes to Prevent and Solve Being Overweight: Burn Fat Fast by Using Proper Dieting and Smart Nutrition

By

Joe Correa CSN

48 Acne Solving Meal Recipes: The Fast and Natural Path to Fixing Your Acne Problems in Less Than 10 Days!

By

Joe Correa CSN

41 Alzheimer's Preventing Meal Recipes: Reduce or Eliminate Your Alzheimer's Condition in 30 Days or Less!

By

Joe Correa CSN

70 Effective Breast Cancer Meal Recipes: Prevent and Fight Breast Cancer with Smart Nutrition and Powerful Foods

By

Joe Correa CSN